THE ULTIMATE
MINNESOTA TWINS
TRIVIA BOOK

A Collection of Amazing Trivia Quizzes
and Fun Facts for Die-Hard Twins Fans!

Ray Walker

Exclusive Free Book

Crazy Sports Stories

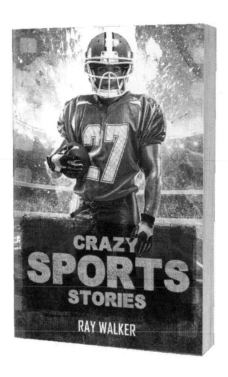

As a thank you for getting a copy of this book I would like to offer you a free copy of my book Crazy Sports Stories which comes packed with interesting stories from your favorite sports such as Football, Hockey, Baseball, Basketball and more.

Grab your free copy over at
RayWalkerMedia.com/Bonus

CONTENTS

INTRODUCTION

Previously known as the Washington Senators and Washington Nationals, the Minnesota Twins were established in 1901. No matter their name, or where they have been located, they have consistently proven themselves to be a team that fights hard and is a force to be reckoned with in the MLB.

They currently hold three World Series championships, which they won in 1924, 1987, and 1991 (which was their most recent appearance), have won six American League pennants, eight AL Central Division titles, four AL West Division titles, and one wild card berth.

The Minnesota Twins have retired the numbers of Harmon Killebrew, Tony Oliva, Joe Mauer, Tom Kelly, Kent Hrbek, Bert Blyleven, Rod Carew, Kirby Puckett, and, of course, Jackie Robinson.

The Twins' current home is Target Field, which opened in 2010. They play in one of the most difficult divisions in baseball, the American League Central Division, where they are quite often a threat, alongside the Cleveland Indians, Detroit Tigers, Kansas City Royals, and Chicago White Sox.

1

The thing about baseball is that it is a lot like life. There are good times and bad times, good days, and bad days, but you have to do your absolute best to never give up. The Minnesota Twins have proven that they refuse to give up and that they will do anything they need to do, to bring a championship to the state of Minnesota. Winning is more than possible when you have a storied past like the Minnesota Twins. They have so much captivating history and so many undeniable player legacies to be profoundly proud of.

With such a storied team past which goes back generations and is current as of 2020, you're probably already very knowledgeable as the die-hard Twins fan that you are. Let's test that knowledge to see if you truly are the World's Biggest Twins Fan.

CHAPTER 1:

ORIGINS AND HISTORY

QUIZ TIME!

1. Which of the following team names did the Twins franchise once go by?

    a. Washington Nationals
    b. Washington Senators
    c. Minnesota Triplets
    d. Both A and B

2. In what year was the franchise established?

    a. 1871
    b. 1881
    c. 1901
    d. 1921

3. The Twins' current home stadium is Target Field.

    a. True
    b. False

4. In which division do the Minnesota Twins play?

a. American League East

b. American League Central

c. National League Central

d. National League East

5. The Minnesota Twins have never won a wild card berth.

a. True

b. False

6. How many American League pennants has the franchise?

a. 6

b. 7

c. 8

d. 9

7. Who is the principal owner of the Minnesota Twins?

a. Larry Dolan

b. Hal Steinbrenner

c. Jim Pohlad

d. Arturo Moreno

8. Who is the winningest manager in Minnesota Twins?

a. Ron Gardenhire

b. Bucky Harris

c. Clark Griffith

d. Cookie Lavagetto

9. What is the name of the Minnesota Twins' Triple-A Team and where is it located?

a. Indianapolis Indians

b. Jacksonville Jumbo Shrimp

c. Toledo Mud Hens

d. St. Paul Saints

10. Who was the first manager of the franchise?

    a. Patsy Donovan

    b. Tom Loftus

    c. Jim Manning

    d. George McBride

11. The Minnesota Twins were in the American League West Division from 1969 through 1993.

    a. True

    b. False

12. What is the name of the Twins' spring training home stadium?

    a. Roger Dean Chevrolet Stadium

    b. Hammond Stadium at CenturyLink Sports Complex

    c. Publix Field at Joker Marchant Stadium

    d. LECOM Park

13. How many appearances has the franchise made in the MLB?

    a. 12

    b. 14

    c. 17

    d. 18

14. How many World Series titles have the Minnesota Twins?

    a. 0

    b. 1

c. 3

d. 5

15. The Minnesota Twins' current manager is Rocco Baldelli.

    a. True

    b. False

16. Which was the franchise's first home stadium?

    a. Metropolitan Stadium

    b. Griffith Stadium

    c. National Park

    d. American League Park

17. Who is the current general manager of the Minnesota Twins?

    a. Mike Rizzo

    b. Mike Elias

    c. David Forst

    d. Thad Levine

18. How many American League Central Division titles have the Minnesota Twins?

    a. 6

    b. 8

    c. 9

    d. 10

19. The Twins are named after the Twin Cities area, which includes the two adjoining cities of Minneapolis and St. Paul.

a. True
b. False

20. Derek Falvey is the current CEO and President of the Minnesota Twins.

a. True
b. False

QUIZ ANSWERS

1. D – Both A and B

2. C – 1901

3. A- True

4. B – American League Central

5. B – False (1, in 2017)

6. A – 6

7. C – Jim Pohlad

8. B – Bucky Harris

9. D – St. Paul Saints

10. C – Jim Manning

11. A – True

12. B – Hammond Stadium at CenturyLink Sports Complex

13. C – 17

14. C – 3

15. A – True

16. D – American League Park

17. D – Thad Levine

18. B – 8

19. A – True

20. A – True

DID YOU KNOW?

1. The Minnesota Twins franchise has had 31 managers Jim Manning, Tom Loftus, Malachi Kittridge, Patsy Donovan, Jake Stahl, Joe Cantillon, Jimmy McAleer, Clark Griffith, George McBride, Clyde Milan, Donie Bush, Bucky Harris, Walter Johnson, Joe Cronin, Ossie Bluege, Joe Kuhel, Chuck Dressen, Cookie Lavagetto, Sam Mele, Cal Ermer, Billy Martin, Bill Rigney, Frank Quilici, Gene Mauch, Johnny Goryl, Billy Gardner, Ray Miller, Tom Kelly, Ron Gardenhire, Paul Molitor, and Rocco Baldelli.

2. The Minnesota Twins' current manager, Rocco Baldelli, was an MLB outfielder from 2003 to 2010 with the Tampa Bay Rays and Boston Red Sox. He also spent three years in the Tampa Bay organization as a roving minor-league instructor and special assistant to baseball operations. He was named the Rays' first-base coach before the 2014 season and was promoted to major league field coordinator in November 2017. At 38 years old, he was the youngest manager to win the AL Manager of the Year Award.

3. Bucky Harris is the Minnesota Twins' all-time winningest manager with a record of 1,336-1,416 (.485) W-L%. Harris managed the Washington Senators from 1924 to 1928, 1935 to 1942, and 1950 to 1954.

4. Jim Pohlad is the current principal owner of the Minnesota Twins. Upon the death of his father, Carl, on January 5, 2009, he inherited ownership of the Twins franchise.

5. The Minnesota Twins franchise has hosted five MLB All-Star Games, in 1937 and 1956 at Griffith Park, in 1965 at Metropolitan Stadium, in 1985 at Hubert H. Humphrey Metrodome, and in 2014 at Target Field.

6. Pitchers for the franchise have thrown 7 no-hitters. The first was thrown by Walter Johnson in 1920 and the most recent was thrown by Francisco Liriano in 2011. There have been no perfect games in franchise history so far.

7. The franchise has 19 American League batting champions so far in franchise history.

8. The Minnesota Twins' Double-A team is the Wichita Wind Surge. High Single-A is the Cedar Rapids Kernels. Low Single-A is the Fort Myers Mighty Mussels.

9. The Minnesota Twins' current mascot is named "T.C. Bear."

10. The Minnesota Twins have retired eight numbers so far in franchise history, nine including Jackie Robinson's No. 42, which is retired throughout MLB. The player who most recently had his number retired was Joe Mauer in 2019.

CHAPTER 2:

JERSEYS AND NUMBERS

QUIZ TIME!

1. In 1973, the Minnesota Twins wore polyester pullover uniforms. These polyester uniforms also included a powder blue road look.

   a. True
   b. False

2. What are the Minnesota Twins' official team colors?

   a. Navy blue, fire engine red, gold, and gray
   b. Navy blue, fire engine red, Minnesota Kasota gold, and white
   c. Navy blue, scarlet red, Minnesota Kasota gold, and white
   d. Baby blue, scarlet red, gold, and white

3. In 2006, the Minnesota Twins wore sleeveless home uniforms with navy undershirts. They wore this look until 2010.

a. True

b. False

4. Which of the following numbers has NOT retired by the franchise?

   a. 3

   b. 7

   c. 29

   d. 33

5. What number does Jose Berríos currently wear as a member of the Minnesota Twins?

   a. 7

   b. 17

   c. 19

   d. 29

6. What number did Rod Carew wear during his time with the Minnesota Twins?

   a. 9

   b. 19

   c. 29

   d. 39

7. Harmon Killebrew wore the Nos. 25, 12, and 3 during his time with the Washington Senators/Minnesota Twins.

   a. True

   b. False

8. Alex Busenitz, Luis Perdomo, and which other player, are the only three Minnesota Twins players to have ever worn No. 67 in franchise history?

    a. Hector Santiago
    b. Max Kepler
    c. Liam Hendricks
    d. Doug Mientkiewicz

9. Who is the only Minnesota Twins player ever to wear the uniform No. 99?

    a. Buddy Boshers
    b. Brian Fuentes
    c. Ryan Eades
    d. Logan Morrison

10. No Minnesota Twins player has ever won the uniform No. 0.

    a. True
    b. False

11. What number did Joe Mauer wear as a member of the Minnesota Twins?

    a. 3
    b. 7
    c. 17
    d. 33

12. What number did Kirby Puckett wear as a member of the Minnesota Twins?

a. 13
b. 18
c. 24
d. 34

13. Brad Radke wore the Nos. 22 and 59 during his time with the Minnesota Twins.

    a. True
    b. False

14. What number did Bert Blyleven wear as a member of the Minnesota Twins?

    a. 8
    b. 18
    c. 28
    d. 38

15. What number did Tony Oliva wear as a member of the Minnesota Twins?

    a. 6
    b. 25
    c. 37
    d. Both A and C

16. What number did Kent Hrbek wear as a member of the Minnesota Twins?

    a. 14
    b. 26
    c. 35
    d. Both A and B

17. During his time with the Minnesota Twins, what number did Chuck Knoblauch wear?

    a. 3
    b. 11
    c. 22
    d. 33

18. What number did Johan Santana wear with the Minnesota Twins?

    a. 27
    b. 37
    c. 47
    d. 57

19. What number did Jim Perry wear as a member of the Minnesota Twins?

    a. 11
    b. 21
    c. 31
    d. 41

20. Camilo Pascual wore the Nos. 27 and 17 during his time with the Washington Senators/Minnesota Twins.

    a. True
    b. False

QUIZ ANSWERS

1. A - True
2. C – Navy blue, scarlet red, Minnesota Kasota gold, and white
3. A – True
4. D – 33
5. B – 17
6. C – 29
7. A – True
8. B – Max Kepler
9. D – Logan Morrison
10. B – False (Junior Ortiz wore it in 1990-1991.)
11. B – 7
12. D – 34
13. A – True
14. C – 28
15. D – Both A and C
16. D – Both A and B
17. B – 11
18. D – 57
19. C – 31
20. A – True

DID YOU KNOW?

1. The Minnesota Twins have retired nine numbers Harmon Killebrew (No. 3), Tony Oliva (No. 6), Joe Mauer (No. 7), Tom Kelly (No. 10), Kent Hrbek (No. 14), Bert Blyleven (No. 28), Rod Carew (No. 29), Kirby Puckett (No. 34), and Jackie Robinson (No. 42).

2. During his time with the Washington Senators/Minnesota Twins, Jim Kaat wore Nos. 21 and 36.

3. Bob Allison wore Nos. 15, 26, and 4 during his time with the Washington Senators/Minnesota Twins.

4. During his time with the Minnesota Twins, Glen Perkins wore Nos. 60 and 15.

5. During his time with the Minnesota Twins, Joe Nathan wore No. 36.

6. During his time with the Minnesota Twins, Brian Dozier wore Nos. 2 and 20.

7. Jackie Robinson's No. 42 is retired by the Minnesota Twins as well as the MLB as a whole. No Twins or MLB player will ever wear No. 42 again. The Yankees' Mariano Rivera was the final player to wear it.

8. During his time with the Minnesota Twins, Michael Cuddyer wore No. 5.

9. During his time with the Minnesota Twins, Justin Morneau wore Nos. 27 and 33.

10. During his time with the Minnesota Twins, Terry Steinbach wore No. 36.

CHAPTER 3:

FRYING DUTCHMAN

QUIZ TIME!

1. What is Bert Blyleven's full name?

    a. Albert Richard Blyleven

    b. Richard Albert Blyleven

    c. Aalbert Rik Blyleven

    d. Rik Aalbert Blyleven

2. Bert Blyleven played his entire 22-season MLB career with the Minnesota Twins.

    a. True

    b. False

3. Where was Bert Blyleven born?

    a. Garden Grove, California

    b. Amsterdam, Netherlands

    c. Zeist, Netherlands

    d. Anaheim, California

4. When was Bert Blyleven born?

a. April 6, 1941

b. April 6, 1951

c. August 6, 1941

d. August 6, 1951

5. Bert Blyleven did NOT win a World Series championship.

   a. True

   b. False

6. How many MLB All-Star Games was Bert Blyleven named to in his 22-season MLB career?

   a. 0

   b. 1

   c. 2

   d. 4

7. What year was Bert Blyleven inducted into the National Baseball Hall of Fame?

   a. 1997

   b. 2002

   c. 2011

   d. 2012

8. Bert Blyleven missed the 1991 MLB season due to injury.

   a. True

   b. False

9. How many seasons did Bert Blyleven spend with the Minnesota Twins?

   a. 8

   b. 9

c. 10

~~d. 11~~

10. How many times Bert Blyleven named the American League Player of the Week?

    a. 1
    b. 2
    c. 3
    d. 4

11. What is Bert Blyleven's career ERA?

    a. 3.01
    b. 3.11
    c. 3.31
    d. 3.41

12. Bert Blyleven did NOT win a Cy Young Award during his MLB career.

    a. True
    b. False

13. How old was Bert Blyleven when he made his MLB debut?

    a. 18
    b. 19
    c. 21
    d. 23

14. Bert Blyleven's final MLB game played was on October 4, 1992, against the Texas Rangers.

a. True

b. False

15. How many strikeouts did Bert Blyleven record in his 22-season MLB career?

a. 3,401

b. 3,501

c. 3,601

d. 3,701

16. How many innings did Bert Blyleven pitch?

a. 4,753.0

b. 4,859.2

c. 4,970.0

d. 5,070.1

17. Bert Blyleven's career WAR is 94.5.

a. True

b. False

18. In high school, Bert Blyleven participated in baseball and which other sport?

a. Tennis

b. Basketball

c. Football

d. Cross country

19. What year did Bert Blyleven lead the American League in strikeouts?

a. 1975

b. 1985

c. 1989

d. 1990

20. Bert Blyleven was a color analyst for Minnesota Twins games from 1996-2020.

   a. True

   b. False

QUIZ ANSWERS

1. D – Rik Aalbert Blyleven
2. B – False (Twins, Cleveland Indians, Pittsburgh Pirates, California Angels, Texas Rangers)
3. C – Zeist, Netherlands
4. B – April 6, 1951
5. B – False (2)
6. C – 2
7. C – 2011
8. A – True
9. D – 11
10. C – 3
11. C – 3.31
12. A – True
13. B – 19
14. A – True
15. D – 3,701
16. C – 4,970.0
17. A - True
18. D – Cross Country
19. B – 1985
20. A – True

DID YOU KNOW?

1. As a member of the Texas Rangers, Bert Blyleven pitched a no-hitter on September 22, 1977. against the California Angels.

2. Bert Blyleven was not inducted into the National Baseball Hall of Fame until his 14th time on the ballot. He got 79.7% of the vote.

3. Bert Blyleven served as the pitching coach for the Netherlands team during the 2009 World Baseball Classic.

4. Bert Blyleven was given the nickname "Frying Dutchman" because he liked to set his teammates' shoelaces on fire as a practical joke.

5. Bert Blyleven did not know his real name until he was married. Since he was born, he had believed his name was "Rikaalbert" when in reality it is "Rik Aalbert."

6. Bert Blyleven finished his 22-season MLB career with a pitching record of 287-250.

7. Bert Blyleven's ERA with the Texas Rangers was 2.74, which remains the best ERA in Texas Rangers history.

8. Blyleven pitched 20 no-decisions in 1979, which are the most in a season by a starting pitcher in MLB.

9. Bert Blyleven started 685 games and played in 692 games.

10. Blyleven was named the 1970 American League Rookie Pitcher of the Year by *The Sporting News.*

CHAPTER 4:

CATCHY NICKNAMES

QUIZ TIME!

1. What nickname did Bert Blyleven go by?

    a. Bly Bly Bly

    b. Leventate

    c. Frying Dutchman

    d. BertnErnie

2. Walter Johnson went by the nicknames "Barney" and "The Big Train."

    a. True

    b. False

3. "Goose" was a nickname. What was Goose Goslin's full name?

    a. Alexander Lars Goslin

    b. Lars Alexander Goslin

    c. Allen Leon Goslin

    d. Leon Allen Goslin

4. What nickname does Kent Hrbek go by?

   a. Kent Stop
   b. Big K
   c. Herbie
   d. Beck

5. "Buddy" was a nickname. What was Buddy Myer's full name?

   a. Solomon Charles Myer
   b. Charles Solomon Myer
   c. Chester Sean Myer
   d. Sean Chester Myer

6. Which nickname did Clyde Milan go by?

   a. Crushin' Clyde
   b. King Milan
   c. Horsefoot
   d. Deerfoot

7. Chuck Knoblauch goes by the nicknames "Knobby" and "Skippy."

   a. True
   b. False

8. What is "Buddy" Lewis' full name?

   a. Kyle Joseph Lewis
   b. Joseph Kyle Lewis
   c. John Kelly Lewis
   d. Kelly John Lewis

9. What nickname does Jim Kaat go by?

    a. Slim Jim
    b. Kitty
    c. Circle K
    d. Six Foot Four Jim

10. What is former Twins' manager "Bucky" Harris' full name?

    a. Richard Steven Harris
    b. Steven Richard Harris
    c. Raymond Stanley Harris
    d. Stanley Raymond Harris

11. What nickname did Gary Gaetti go by?

    a. The Rat
    b. G – Man
    c. King G
    d. Both A and B

12. Camilo Pascual goes by the nicknames "Patato Pequeño," "Camile," and "Little Potato."

    a. True
    b. False

13. Which nickname does Frank Viola go by?

    a. Frankie Flames
    b. Sweet Music
    c. Music Man
    d. Flaming Frank

14. What nickname does David Ortiz popularly go by?

   a. Little O
   b. Little Papi
   c. Big Papi
   d. Big Daddy

15. Zoilo Versalles went by the nickname "Zorro."

   a. True
   b. False

16. What nickname does Torii Hunter go by?

   a. Thor
   b. Black Panther
   c. Iron Man
   d. Spiderman

17. Denard Span goes by the nicknames "Spanny," "D-Span," and "Spaniard."

   a. True
   b. False

18. What is Jim Dwyer's nickname?

   a. Charlie Brown
   b. Woodstock
   c. Snoopy
   d. Pig Pen

19. What is A.J. Pierzynski's full name?

   a. Austin James Pierzynski
   b. Arthur Jacob Pierzynski

c. Anthony John Pierzynski

d. Adam Joseph Pierzynski

20. Nelson Cruz goes by the nickname "Boomstick."

a. True

b. False

QUIZ ANSWERS

1. C – Frying Dutchman

2. A- True

3. D – Leon Allen Goslin

4. C – Herbie

5. B – Charles Solomon Myer

6. D – Deerfoot

7. A – True

8. C – John Kelly Lewis

9. B – Kitty

10. D – Stanley Raymond Harris

11. D – Both A and B

12. A – True

13. B – Sweet Music

14. C – Big Papi

15. A - True

16. D – Spiderman

17. A – True

18. D – Pig Pen

19. C – Anthony John Pierzynski

20. A – True

DID YOU KNOW?

1. Doug Mientkiewicz goes by the nickname "Eye Chart."

2. Billy Gardner went by the nicknames "Whitey" and "Shotgun."

3. Dutch Leonard's full name was Emil John Leonard.

4. Eddie Guardado goes by the nickname "Everyday Eddie."

5. Kurt Suzuki goes by the nickname "Zuk."

6. Paul Molitor goes by the nickname "The Ignitor."

7. Gregg Olson goes by the nicknames, "Otter."

8. Glen Perkins goes by the nickname "Perk."

9. Chili Davis's full name is Charles Theodore Davis.

10. Don Baylor went by the nicknames "Groove" and "The Sneak Thief."

CHAPTER 5:

CAREW

QUIZ TIME!

1. What is Rod Carew's full name?

    a. Rodney Charles Carew

    b. Rodney Christopher Carew

    c. Rodney Cline Carew

    d. Rodney Carter Carew

2. Rod Carew. played his entire 19-season MLB career with the Minnesota Twins.

    a. True

    b. False

3. Where was Rod Carew born?

    a. Cerro Punta, Panama

    b. Colón, Panama

    c. David, Panama

    d. Gatun, Panama

4. When was Rod Carew born?

a. October 1, 1945
b. October 1, 1955
c. January 1, 1945
d. January 1, 1955

5. In 2016, the AL batting title was renamed the "Rod Carew American League batting title."

a. True
b. False

6. How many total, and consecutive, MLB All-Star Games was Rod Carew named to?

a. 13
b. 15
c. 18
d. 19

7. Rod Carew was named the American League Rookie of the Year in which year?

a. 1966
b. 1967
c. 1968
d. 1969

8. Rod Carew did NOT win a World Series championship during his career.

a. True
b. False

9. What year was Rod Carew inducted into the National Baseball Hall of Fame with 90.5% of the vote?

   a. 1990
   b. 1991
   c. 1993
   d. 1995

10. How many Gold Glove Awards did Rod Carew win?

   a. 0
   b. 1
   c. 2
   d. 3

11. How many times did Rod Carew win the American League batting title?

   a. 4
   b. 6
   c. 7
   d. 8

12. Rod Carew was born on a train. He was delivered on the train by a doctor named Dr. Rodney Cline, which is who his mother named him after.

   a. True
   b. False

13. Rod Carew was named the American League MVP in which year?

   a. 1972
   b. 1974

c. 1975

d. 1977

14. Rod Carew was inducted into the Minnesota Twins Hall of Fame in 2000.

a. True

b. False

15. Rod Carew was named the Major League Player of the Year in which year?

a. 1970

b. 1973

c. 1977

d. 1980

16. How many home runs did Rod Carew hit?

a. 92

b. 102

c. 202

d. 302

17. Rod Carew's career batting average is .328.

a. True

b. False

18. What year was Rod Carew's No. 29 retired by the Minnesota Twins?

a. 1986

b. 1987

c. 1989

d. 1992

19. How many bases did Rod Carew steal?

    a. 53

    b. 153

    c. 253

    d. 353

20. There is a statue of Rod Carew's daughter Michelle outside of Angel Stadium. She died of leukemia in 1996 at 18 years old.

    a. True

    b. False

QUIZ ANSWERS

1. C – Rodney Cline Carew

2. B – False (Twins, 12 years; California Angels, 7 years)

3. D – Gatun, Panama

4. A – October 1, 1945

5. A - True

6. C – 18

7. B – 1967

8. A – True

9. B – 1991

10. A – 0

11. C – 7

12. A – True

13. D – 1977

14. A – True

15. C – 1977

16. A – 92

17. A - True

18. B – 1987

19. D – 353

20. A – True

DID YOU KNOW?

1. Rod Carew was inducted into the Hispanic Heritage Baseball Museum Hall of Fame in 2010.

2. Rod Carew's uniform No. 29 was retired by the California/ Los Angeles Angels in 1986.

3. Rod Carew's 3,053 hits is 27th all-time in the MLB.

4. During the 1960s, Carew served in the United States Marine Corps Reserve as a combat engineer.

5. Carew was hired as the California Angels' hitting coach on November 5, 1991, and served in a similar position with the Milwaukee Brewers. He helped to develop hitters like Garret Anderson, Jim Edmonds, and Tim Salmon. He has also worked as a minor league and spring training hitting and base running coach for the Minnesota Twins and as an international youth baseball instructor for the MLB.

6. On January 19, 2004, Panama City's National Stadium was renamed "Rod Carew Stadium."

7. Rod Carew's seven American League batting titles is the second most in history, behind only Ty Cobb.

8. Rod Carew's batting average in 1977 with the Twins was .388, a Twins record.

9. On August 4, 1985, Rod Carew became the 16th member of the 3,000-hit club.

10. Rod Carew had a heart transplant on December 15, 2016, following a massive heart attack while on a golf course in California. Carew's transplanted heart was donated by former NFL tight end Konrad Reuland. Reuland, who suffered a fatal brain aneurism, had attended middle school with Carew's children.

CHAPTER 6:

STATISTICALLY SPEAKING

QUIZ TIME!

1. With the franchise record, how many home runs did Harmon Killebrew hit during his MLB career?

    a. 529

    b. 539

    c. 549

    d. 559

2. Pitcher Walter Johnson has the most wins in Minnesota Twins franchise history with 417.

    a. True

    b. False

3. Which pitcher holds the Minnesota Twins record for most career shutouts thrown with 110?

    a. Camilo Pascual

    b. Walter Johnson

    c. Bert Blyleven

    d. Jim Kaat

4. Which Minnesota Twins batter holds the single season record for strikeouts with 178?

    a. Byron Buxton
    b. Brian Dozier
    c. Miguel Sano
    d. Carlos Gomez

5. Walter Johnson has the most strikeouts in Minnesota Twins franchise history with how many?

    a. 3,209
    b. 3,309
    c. 3,409
    d. 3,509

6. Who has the most stolen bases in franchise history with 495?

    a. Sam Rice
    b. Rod Carew
    c. Clyde Milan
    d. George Case

7. Joe Nathan holds the record for most saves in Minnesota Twins history with 260.

    a. True
    b. False

8. Who holds the Minnesota Twins record for being intentionally walked with 156?

    a. Joe Mauer
    b. Harmon Killebrew

c. Rod Carew

d. Tony Oliva

9. Who holds the Minnesota Twins franchise record for home runs in a single season with 49?

   a. Roy Sievers

   b. Nelson Cruz

   c. Brian Dozier

   d. Harmon Killebrew

10. Which batter holds the single season Minnesota Twins record for hits with 239?

    a. Paul Molitor

    b. Rod Carew

    c. Kirby Puckett

    d. Sam Rice

11. Which two players are tied for the single season Minnesota Twins record for double plays grounded into with 28 total each?

    a. Kirby Puckett and Michael Cuddyer

    b. Harmon Killebrew and Kirby Puckett

    c. Harmon Killebrew and Trevor Plouffe

    d. Kirby Puckett and Trevor Plouffe

12. Harmon Killebrew holds the record for the most sacrifice flies in franchise history with 75

    a. True

    b. False

13. Walter Johnson threw the highest number of wild pitches in franchise history with how many?

    a. 114
    b. 134
    c. 144
    d. 154

14. Goose Goslin and Cristian Guzman are tied for the franchise's single season record for triples with how many did?

    a. 16
    b. 19
    c. 20
    d. 22

15. Which hitter has the most walks in Minnesota Twins franchise history with 1,505?

    a. Harmon Killebrew
    b. Eddie Yost
    c. Joe Judge
    d. Joe Mauer

16. Which hitter holds the all-time franchise record for best overall batting average at .334?

    a. Heinie Manush
    b. Rod Carew
    c. Goose Goslin
    d. Cecil Travis

17. Sam Rice holds the franchise record for most runs scored with 1,466.

    a. True
    b. False

18. Sam Rice has the most plate appearances all-time in franchise history with how many?

    a. 9,693
    b. 9,793
    c. 9,893
    d. 9,993

19. Which pitcher holds the Minnesota Twins franchise record for most saves in a single season with 47?

    a. Eddie Guardado
    b. Rick Aguilera
    c. Jeff Reardon
    d. Joe Nathan

20. Walter Johnson holds the franchise record for most losses by a pitcher with 279.

    a. True
    b. False

QUIZ ANSWERS

1. D – 559

2. A - True

3. B – Walter Johnson

4. C – Miguel Sano (2016)

5. D – 3,509

6. C – Clyde Milan

7. A – True

8. B – Harmon Killebrew

9. D – Harmon Killebrew (1964 and 1969)

10. B – Rod Carew (1977)

11. C – Harmon Killebrew and Trevor Plouffe (1970 and 2015)

12. A – True

13. D – 154

14. C – 20 (Goslin – 1925 and Guzman – 2000)

15. A – Harmon Killebrew

16. B – Rod Carew

17. A – True

18. C – 9,893

19. D – Joe Nathan (2009)

20. A – True

DID YOU KNOW?

1. Walter Johnson threw the most innings in franchise history with 5,914.1, coming in second is Jim Kaat, who threw 3,014.1 innings.

2. Rod Carew had the best single season batting average in franchise history at .388 in 1977. Coming in second is Goose Goslin, whose batting average was .379 in 1928.

3. Alexi Casilla holds the franchise record for stolen base percentage with 88.75% success. Clyde Milan holds the franchise record for stolen bases with 495 and Sam Rice holds the franchise record for the most times caught stealing at 142 times.

4. Harmon Killebrew has the most extra-base hits in franchise history with 860. Second on the list is Sam Rice with 695.

5. Harmon Killebrew holds the Minnesota Twins franchise record for at-bats per home run at 14.0. This means that Killebrew hit a home run about every 14 at-bats.

6. Johan Santana holds the Minnesota Twins franchise record for strikeouts per 9 innings pitched at 9.497. This means that, during his time with the Twins, Santana recorded about 9-10 strikeouts in every 9 innings that he pitched.

7. Kid Elberfeld holds the single season franchise record for the most hit by pitches with 25 in 1911. Bill Carrick,

Walter Johnson, and Casey Patten are tied for the single season Minnesota Twins record for most batters hit with 20 each.

8. Sam Rice holds the franchise record for career doubles with 479. Second on the list is Joe Mauer with 428.

9. Walter Johnson holds the franchise's single season record for wins with 36 in 1913. Bob Groom and Happy Townsend are tied for the franchise's single season record for most losses with 26 each.

10. Walter Johnson holds the single season franchise record for most strikeouts with 313 in 1910.

CHAPTER 7:

THE TRADE MARKET

QUIZ TIME!

1. On November 3, 1988, the Minnesota Twins traded Kevin Trudeau, and which other player, to the California Angels in exchange for Paul Sorrento, Mike Cook, and Rob Wassenaar?

   a. Tippy Martinez
   b. Bert Blyleven
   c. Frank Viola
   d. Kent Hrbek

2. On May 12, 1982, the Minnesota Twins traded Doug Corbett and Rob Wilfong to which team, in exchange for Tom Brunansky, Mike Walters, and $400,000?

   a. Boston Red Sox
   b. Milwaukee Brewers
   c. California Angels
   d. St. Louis Cardinals

3. The Minnesota Twins have made six trades with the Arizona.

    a. True
    b. False

4. On February 6, 1998, the Minnesota Twins traded Chuck Knoblauch to which team, in exchange for Brian Buchanan, Cristian Guzman, Eric Milton, Danny Mota, and cash considerations?

    a. San Francisco Giants
    b. Cincinnati Reds
    c. Kansas City Royals
    d. New York Yankees

5. The Minnesota Twins have made six trades with the Colorado.

    a. True
    b. False

6. On November 29, 1972, the Minnesota Twins traded Wayne Granger to which team, in exchange for John Cumberland and Larry Hisle?

    a. St. Louis Cardinals
    b. Houston Astros
    c. Cincinnati Reds
    d. Montreal Expos

7. On December 3, 2003, the Minnesota Twins traded which player to the Philadelphia Phillies, in exchange for Nick

Punto, Carlos Silva, and a player to be named later (Bobby Korecky)?

a. Eddie Guardado
b. Eric Milton
c. Kyle Lohse
d. LaTroy Hawkins

8. On May 2, 1963, the Minnesota Twins traded Jack Kralick to which team, in exchange for Jim Perry?

a. Atlanta Braves
b. Oakland A's
c. Baltimore Orioles
d. Cleveland Indians

9. On December 4, 1964, the Minnesota Twins traded Gerry Arrigo to which team, in exchange for César Tovar?

a. Texas Rangers
b. Chicago White Sox
c. Cincinnati Reds
d. New York Mets

10. The Minnesota Twins have made only four trades with the Florida/Miami.

a. True
b. False

11. On July 31, 1989, the Minnesota Twins traded Frank Viola to which team, in exchange for Rick Aguilera, Tim Drummond, Kevin Tapani, David West, and a player to be named later (Jack Savage)?

a. New York Yankees

b. Cincinnati Reds

c. Toronto Blue Jays

d. New York Mets

12. The Minnesota Twins have made only nine trades with the San Diego.

    a. True

    b. False

13. How many trades have the Minnesota Twins made with the Atlanta?

    a. 15

    b. 17

    c. 20

    d. 22

14. The Minnesota Twins have made only eight trades with the Toronto Blue.

    a. True

    b. False

15. On November 14, 2003, the Minnesota Twins traded A.J. Pierzynski and cash considerations to which team, in exchange for Joe Nathan, Francisco Liriano, and Boof Bonser?

    a. Chicago White Sox

    b. San Francisco Giants

    c. Atlanta Braves

    d. St. Louis Cardinals

16. On February 2, 2008, the Minnesota Twins traded which player to the New York Mets in exchange for Carlos Gomez, Deolis Guerra, Philip Humber and Kevin Mulvey?

    a. Ramon Ortiz
    b. Glen Perkins
    c. Johan Santana
    d. Carlos Silva

17. On January 16, 1986, the Minnesota Twins traded Tim Teufel and Pat Crosby to which team, in exchange for Billy Beane, Joe Klink, and Bill Latham?

    a. New York Mets
    b. San Diego Padres
    c. Detroit Tigers
    d. Oakland A's

18. On November 11, 2015, the Minnesota Twins traded which player, to the New York Yankees in exchange for John Ryan Murphy?

    a. Trevor Plouffe
    b. Aaron Hicks
    c. Max Kepler
    d. Glen Perkins

19. On May 12, 1982, the Minnesota Twins traded Roger Erickson and Butch Wynegar to which team, in exchange for Pete Filson, Larry Milbourne, John Pacella, and cash considerations?

    a. California Angels
    b. Chicago White Sox

c. Kansas City Royals

d. New York Yankees

20. The Minnesota Twins have made five trades with the Tampa Bay Rays/Devil Rays.

a. True

b. False

QUIZ ANSWERS

1. B – Bert Blyleven

2. C – California Angels

3. A – True

4. D – New York Yankees

5. A- True

6. A – St. Louis Cardinals

7. B – Eric Milton

8. D – Cleveland Indians

9. C – Cincinnati Reds

10. A- True

11. D – New York Mets

12. A – True

13. B – 17

14. A – True

15. B – San Francisco Giants

16. C – Johan Santana

17. A – New York Mets

18. B – Aaron Hicks

19. D – New York Yankees

20. A- True

DID YOU KNOW?

1. On February 3, 1979, the Minnesota Twins traded Rod Carew to the California Angels in exchange for Dave Engle, Paul Hartzell, Brad Havens, and Ken Landreaux.

2. On November 6, 2009, the Minnesota Twins traded Carlos Gomez to the Milwaukee Brewers in exchange for J.J. Hardy.

3. On July 7, 1995, the Minnesota Twins traded Scott Erickson to the Baltimore Orioles in exchange for Scott Klingenbeck and a player to be named later (Kimera Bartee).

4. On December 10, 1969, the Minnesota Twins traded Dean Chance, Bob Miller, Graig Nettles, and Ted Uhlaender to the Cleveland Indians in exchange for Luis Tiant and Stan Williams.

5. On December 9, 2010, the Minnesota Twins traded J.J. Hardy and Brendan Harris to the Baltimore Orioles in exchange for Jim Hoey and Brett Jacobson.

6. On November 28, 2007, the Minnesota Twins traded Matt Garza, Jason Bartlett, and Eddie Morlan to the Tampa Bay Devil Rays in exchange for Brendan Harris, Jason Pridie, and Delmon Young.

7. On December 13, 1999, the Minnesota Twins traded Jared Camp to the Florida Marlins in exchange for Johan Santana.

8. On June 1, 1976, the Minnesota Twins traded Bert Blyleven and Danny Thompson to the Texas Rangers in exchange for Roy Smalley, Bill Singer, Jim Gideon, Mike Cubbage, and $250,000.

9. The Minnesota Twins have made nine trades with the Houston.

10. The Minnesota Twins have made only four trades with the Kansas City.

CHAPTER 8:

DRAFT DAY

QUIZ TIME!

1. Bert Blyleven was drafted by the Minnesota Twins in the third round of the MLB draft in which year?

   a. 1967
   b. 1968
   c. 1969
   d. 1970

2. Brad Radke was drafted by the Minnesota Twins in the eighth round of the MLB draft in which year?

   a. 1988
   b. 1989
   c. 1990
   d. 1991

3. With which overall pick, in the first round of the 2001 MLB draft, did the Minnesota Twins select Joe Mauer?

   a. 1st
   b. 2nd

c. 5th

d. 9th

4. With which overall pick, in the first round of the 2007 MLB draft, did the Minnesota Twins select Kirby Puckett?

    a. 1st

    b. 3rd

    c. 8th

    d. 12th

5. In the second round of the 2004 MLB draft, which team selected Kurt Suzuki?

    a. Atlanta Braves

    b. Minnesota Twins

    c. San Diego Padres

    d. Oakland A's

6. Kent Hrbek was drafted by the Minnesota Twins in which round of the 1978 MLB draft?

    a. 4th

    b. 10th

    c. 17th

    d. 20th

7. Chuck Knoblauch was drafted by the Minnesota Twins in the first round, 25th overall in the 1989 MLB draft.

    a. True

    b. False

8. Brian Dozier was drafted by the Minnesota Twins in which round of the 2009 MLB draft?

a. 5th

b. 8th

c. 14th

d. 19th

9. With which overall pick, in the first round of the 1993 MLB draft, did the Minnesota Twins select Torii Hunter?

a. 1st

b. 6th

c. 16th

d. 20th

10. Justin Morneau was drafted by the Minnesota Twins in the third round of the 1999 MLB draft.

a. True

b. False

11. A.J. Pierzynski was drafted by the Minnesota Twins in which round of the 1994 MLB draft?

a. 2nd

b. 3rd

c. 6th

d. 10th

12. Eddie Guardado was drafted by the Minnesota Twins in the second round of the 1990 MLB draft.

a. True

b. False

13. With which overall pick in the first round of the 1997 MLB draft, did the Minnesota Twins select Michael Cuddyer.

    a. 5th
    b. 7th
    c. 9th
    d. 11th

14. With which overall pick, in the first round of the 1979 MLB draft, did the Minnesota Twins select Gary Gaetti?

    a. 4th
    b. 5th
    c. 7th
    d. 11th

15. Frank Viola was drafted by the Minnesota Twins in which round of the 1981 MLB draft?

    a. 2nd
    b. 3rd
    c. 12th
    d. 13th

16. Terry Steinbach was drafted by which team in the ninth round of the 1983 MLB draft?

    a. Minnesota Twins
    b. Houston Astros
    c. Oakland A's
    d. Baltimore Orioles

17. With which overall pick, in the first round of the 2012 MLB draft, did the Minnesota Twins select Jose Berríos?

a. 42nd

b. 32nd

c. 22nd

d. 12th

18. Nick Punto was drafted in the 21st round of the 1998 MLB draft by which team?

    a. Boston Red Sox

    b. Los Angeles Dodgers

    c. Philadelphia Phillies

    d. St. Louis Cardinals

19. With which overall pick, in the first round of the 2004 MLB draft, did the Minnesota Twins select Glen Perkins?

    a. 22nd

    b. 12th

    c. 2nd

    d. 1st

20. Dave Goltz was drafted by the Minnesota Twins in the fifth round of the 1967 MLB draft.

    a. True

    b. False

QUIZ ANSWERS

1. C – 1969

2. D – 1991

3. A – 1st

4. B – 3rd

5. D – Oakland A's

6. C – 17th

7. A – True

8. B – 8th

9. D – 20th

10. A – True

11. B – 3rd

12. B – False (21st round)

13. C – 9th

14. D – 11th

15. A – 2nd

16. C – Oakland A's

17. B – 32nd

18. C – Philadelphia Phillies

19. A – 22nd

20. A – True

DID YOU KNOW?

1. Joe Nathan was drafted in the sixth round of the 1995 MLB draft by the San Francisco Giants.

2. Rick Aguilera was drafted in the third round in the 1983 MLB draft by the New York Mets.

3. Dave Winfield was drafted in the first round, fourth overall pick, of the 1973 MLB draft by the San Diego Padres.

4. Kevin Tapani was drafted in the second round of the 1986 MLB draft by the Oakland A's.

5. Denard Span was drafted in the first round, 20th overall pick, of the 2002 MLB draft by the Minnesota Twins.

6. Jim Thome was drafted in the 13th round of the 1989 MLB draft by the Cleveland Indians.

7. Josh Willingham was drafted in the 17th round of the 2000 MLB draft by the Florida Marlins.

8. Trevor Plouffe was drafted in the first round, 20th overall, of the 2004 MLB draft by the Minnesota Twins.

9. Greg Gagne was drafted in the fifth round of the 1979 MLB draft by the New York Yankees.

10. Tom Brunansky was drafted in the first round, 14th overall, of the 1978 MLB draft by the California Angels.

CHAPTER 9:

ODDS AND ENDS

QUIZ TIME!

1. What was former Twins' outfielder Dave Winfield arrested for stealing while in college?

   a. Snowblower

   b. Bag of chips

   c. Baseball glove

   d. Lawnmower

2. Jim Thome established a fund during his playing days to help put his 10 nieces and nephews through college.

   a. True

   b. False

3. Which former Minnesota Twins player was a groomsman at Joe Mauer's wedding?

   a. Brian Dozier

   b. Justin Morneau

   c. Trevor Plouffe

   d. Glen Perkins

4. Which of the following sports did Brian Dozier NOT receive a varsity letter in during high school?

    a. Football
    b. Basketball
    c. Golf
    d. Hockey

5. When Torii Hunter made the U.S. Junior Olympic team, he could not pay the $500 fee, so he wrote a letter to whom for help, which was accepted?

    a. Rod Carew
    b. Bill Gates
    c. Bill Clinton
    d. George H.W. Bush

6. Former Twin Chip Hale was manager of which team from 2015-2016?

    a. Detroit Tigers
    b. Arizona Diamondbacks
    c. Washington Nationals
    d. Oakland A's

7. Kurt Suzuki has won both the College World Series and the MLB World Series.

    a. True
    b. False

8. Which of the following sitcoms did Frank Viola make an appearance in?

a. King of Queens

b. Fresh Prince of Bel-Air

c. The Big Bang Theory

d. How I Met Your Mother

9. Bert Blyleven starred in which film, as himself?

a. Back to the Future Part III

b. Taking Care of Business

c. Edward Scissorhands

d. The Rookie

10. Eddie Guardado's oldest son, Niko, was a cast member on which 2020 TV series?

a. Good Trouble

b. Ted Lasso

c. Party of Five

d. The Mandalorian

11. LaTroy Hawkins is the godfather of which current NFL quarterback?

a. Russell Wilson, Seattle Mariners

b. Patrick Mahomes, Kansas City Chiefs

c. Aaron Rodgers, Green Bay Packers

d. Kirk Cousins, Minnesota Vikings

12. Michael Cuddyer has been deaf in his left ear since he was 11 years old.

a. True

b. False

13. Which former Twins player is the brother-in-law of fellow former Twin Jason Kubel?

    a. Ricky Nolasco
    b. Aaron Hicks
    c. Sam Fuld
    d. Michael Tonkin

14. During his 16-season MLB career, Kyle Lohse defeated all 30 MLB teams.

    a. True
    b. False

15. Dan Gladden's daughter, Ashley, married the son of which former Twins' teammate?

    a. Greg Gagne
    b. Gary Gaetti
    c. Don Baylor
    d. Kent Hrbek

16. During his nine-season MLB career, Trevor Plouffe played at every position except catcher, pitcher, and center fielder.

    a. True
    b. False

17. What is the name of Jim Kaat's bestselling book?

    a. For the Love of the Game: From the Field to the Broadcast Booth
    b. The Kaat's Out of the Bag

c. Still Pitching: Musings from the Mound and the Microphone

d. Kitty in the Booth

18. Chili Davis was the first player born in which location, to appear in an MLB game?

   a. Hawaii

   b. New Zealand

   c. Alaska

   d. Jamaica

19. Miguel Sano is one of the subjects of the baseball documentary with what title?

   a. Knuckleball

   b. Ballplayer: Pelotero

   c. Catching Hell

   d. Long Shot

20. MLB mistakenly spelled Kendrys Morales' first name as "Kendry" until March 2011.

   a. True

   b. False

QUIZ ANSWERS

1. A – Snowblower

2. A – True

3. B – Justin Morneau

4. D – Hockey

5. C – Bill Clinton

6. B – Arizona Diamondbacks

7. A – True

8. D – *How I Met Your Mother*

9. B – *Taking Care of Business*

10. C – *Party of Five*

11. B – Patrick Mahomes, Kansas City Chiefs

12. A – True

13. D – Michael Tonkin

14. A – True

15. B – Gary Gaetti

16. A – True

17. C – *Still Pitching: Musings from the Mound and the Microphone*

18. D – Jamaica

19. B – *Ballplayer: Pelotero*

20. A – True

DID YOU KNOW?

1. When Bartolo Colón was 42 years old, he became the oldest MLB player to hit his first career home run. At 45 years old, he was the oldest active MLB player and the last active MLB player who had played for the Montreal Expos. He also holds the record for most wins by a pitcher born in Latin America.

2. Nelson Cruz takes a nap before almost every game he plays as a pregame ritual.

3. During his time with the Minnesota Twins, Justin Morneau gave personalized holiday gifts to over 200 Twins employees, including the grounds crew.

4. Former Twins player Pat Mahomes is the father of Kansas City Chiefs quarterback Patrick Mahomes.

5. Former Twin Jim Perry is the brother of MLB Hall of Famer Gaylord Perry.

6. Former Twin Delmon Young is the younger brother of former MLB player Dmitri Young. Dmitri played for the St. Louis Cardinals, Cincinnati Reds, Detroit Tigers, and Washington Nationals.

7. Kent Hrbek hosted a sports TV program called *Kent Hrbek Outdoors* from 2004 to 2010.

8. After Bob Allison's death, the Minnesota Twins created the Bob Allison Award, which is given to a Twins player each season for his determination, hustle, tenacity, competitive spirit, and leadership.

9. Jose Berríos' wife is the sister of the wife of Javier Báez, who plays for the Chicago Cubs.

10. Max Kepler was born in Berlin, Germany. He holds the MLB record for home runs hit by a player born in Germany.

CHAPTER 10:

OUTFIELDERS

QUIZ TIME!

1. Tony Oliva was named the American League Rookie of the Year in which year?

    a. 1962
    b. 1963
    c. 1964
    d. 1965

2. Sam Rice was inducted into the National Baseball Hall of Fame in 1963.

    a. True
    b. False

3. What year was Goose Goslin inducted into the National Baseball Hall of Fame?

    a. 1965
    b. 1966
    c. 1967
    d. 1968

4. Clyde Milan spent his entire 16-season career with the Washington Senators.

   a. True
   b. False

5. Bob Allison was named the American League Rookie of the Year in which year?

   a. 1958
   b. 1959
   c. 1960
   d. 1961

6. How many Gold Glove Awards did Torii Hunter win during his 19-season MLB career?

   a. 7
   b. 8
   c. 9
   d. 10

7. Denard Span played five seasons with the Minnesota Twins.

   a. True
   b. False

8. During his 13-season MLB career, Dan Ford played for the Minnesota Twins, Baltimore Orioles, and which other team?

   a. Oakland A's
   b. California Angels

c. San Diego Padres

d. Los Angeles Dodgers

9. How many seasons did Tom Brunansky spend with the Minnesota Twins?

    a. 6

    b. 7

    c. 8

    d. 9

10. Josh Willingham won his sole Silver Slugger Award in which year, with the Minnesota Twins?

    a. 2010

    b. 2011

    c. 2012

    d. 2013

11. How many MLB All-Star Games was Jimmie Hall named to in his eight-season MLB career?

    a. 0

    b. 1

    c. 2

    d. 3

12. Jim Lemon missed the 1951 and 1952 MLB seasons due to military service.

    a. True

    b. False

13. How many seasons of his MLB career did César Tovar spend with the Minnesota Twins?

    a. 5
    b. 6
    c. 7
    d. 8

14. Jim Holt spent seven years of his MLB career with the Minnesota Twins and three years with which other team?

    a. New York Yankees
    b. Oakland A's
    c. Cincinnati Reds
    d. Los Angeles Dodgers

15. During his 15-season MLB career, Michael Cuddyer played for the Minnesota Twins, New York Mets, and which other team?

    a. Kansas City Royals
    b. Toronto Blue Jays
    c. Colorado Rockies
    d. Texas Rangers

16. How many MLB All-Star Games was Larry Hisle named to in his 14-season MLB career?

    a. 1
    b. 2
    c. 3
    d. 4

17. How many MLB All-Star Games was Gary Ward named to during his 12-season MLB career?

    a. 0
    b. 1
    c. 2
    d. 3

18. How many MLB All-Star Games was Matt Lawton named to in his 12-season MLB career?

    a. 1
    b. 2
    c. 3
    d. 4

19. How many seasons of his MLB career did Jacque Jones spend with the Minnesota Twins?

    a. 6
    b. 7
    c. 8
    d. 9

20. Randy Bush spent his entire 12-season MLB career with the Minnesota Twins.

    a. True
    b. False

QUIZ ANSWERS

1. C – 1964

2. A – True

3. D – 1968

4. A – True

5. B – 1959

6. C – 9

7. A – True

8. B – California Angels

9. B – 7

10. C – 2012

11. C – 2

12. A – True

13. D – 8

14. B – Oakland A's

15. C – Colorado Rockies

16. B – 2

17. C – 2

18. B – 2

19. B – 7

20. A – True

DID YOU KNOW?

1. Tony Oliva spent his entire 15-season MLB career with the Minnesota Twins. He was an American League Rookie of the Year, 8x MLB All-Star, Gold Glove Award winner, and 3x Batting title champion.

2. Torii Hunter spent 12 seasons of his 19-season MLB career with the Minnesota Twins. He also played for the Los Angeles Angels and Detroit Tigers. He was a 5x MLB All-Star, 9x Gold Glove Award winner, and 2x Silver Slugger Award winner.

3. Michael Cuddyer spent 11 seasons of his 15-season MLB career with the Minnesota Twins. He also played for the Colorado Rockies and New York Mets. He was a 2x MLB All-Star, Silver Slugger Award winner, and batting title champion.

4. Denard Span spent 5 seasons of his 11-season MLB career with the Minnesota Twins. He also played for the Washington Nationals, San Francisco Giants, Tampa Bay Rays, and Seattle Mariners.

5. Jimmie Hall spent four seasons of his eight-season MLB career with the Minnesota Twins. He also played for the Chicago Cubs, Cleveland Indians, California Angels, Atlanta Braves, and New York Yankees. He was a 2x MLB All-Star.

6. Randy Bush spent his entire 12-season MLB career with the Minnesota Twins. He was a 2x World Series champion.

7. Jim Lemon spent 10 seasons of his 12-season MLB career with the Washington Senators/Minnesota Twins. He also played for the Cleveland Indians, Philadelphia Phillies, and Chicago White Sox. He was a 2x MLB All-Star.

8. Bob Allison spent his entire 13-season MLB career with the Minnesota Twins. He was an American League Rookie of the Year and 3x MLB All-Star.

9. Matt Lawton spent 7 seasons of his 12-season MLB career with the Minnesota Twins. He also played for the Cleveland Indians, New York Mets, Chicago Cubs, Pittsburgh Pirates, Seattle Mariners, and New York Yankees. He was a 2x MLB All-Star.

10. Gary Ward spent 5 seasons of his 12-season MLB career with the Minnesota Twins. He also played for the Texas Rangers, New York Yankees, and Detroit Tigers. He was a 2x MLB All-Star.

CHAPTER 11:

INFIELDERS

QUIZ TIME!

1. Chuck Knoblauch was named the American League Rookie of the Year in which year?

   a. 1990

   b. 1991

   c. 1992

   d. 1993

2. Kent Hrbek spent his entire 14-season MLB career with the Minnesota Twins.

   a. True

   b. False

3. How many seasons did Joe Judge spend with the Washington Senators?

   a. 15

   b. 16

   c. 18

   d. 20

4. How many MLB All-Star Games was Buddy Myer named to in his 17-season MLB career?

   a. 1
   b. 2
   c. 3
   d. 4

5. What year was Joe Cronin inducted into the National Baseball Hall of Fame?

   a. 1953
   b. 1954
   c. 1955
   d. 1956

6. How many MLB All-Star Games was Cecil Travis named to in his 12-season MLB career?

   a. 1
   b. 2
   c. 3
   d. 4

7. Buddy Lewis missed the 1942, 1943, and 1944 MLB seasons due to military service.

   a. True
   b. False

8. 8. How many Gold Glove Awards did Brian Dozier win during his 9-season MLB career?

   a. 0
   b. 1

c. 2

d. 3

9. How many seasons did Trevor Plouffe spend with the Minnesota Twins?

    a. 4

    b. 5

    c. 6

    d. 7

10. Justin Morneau was named the American League MVP during which season with the Minnesota Twins.

    a. 2005

    b. 2006

    c. 2007

    d. 2008

11. How many Gold Glove Awards did Gary Gaetti win in his 20-season MLB career?

    a. 1

    b. 2

    c. 3

    d. 4

12. Ossie Bluege spent his entire 18-season MLB career with the Washington Senators.

    a. True

    b. False

13. John Castino was named the American League Rookie of the Year in which year?

    a. 1977

    b. 1978

    c. 1979

    d. 1980

14. Zoilo Versalles was named American League MVP in which year?

    a. 1961

    b. 1962

    c. 1963

    d. 1964

15. How many MLB All-Star Games was Rich Rollins named to in his 10-season MLB career?

    a. 0

    b. 1

    c. 2

    d. 3

16. Nick Punto spent seven seasons with the Minnesota Twins.

    a. True

    b. False

17. How many MLB All-Star Games was David Ortiz named to during his 20-season MLB career?

    a. 7

    b. 8

c. 9

d. 10

18. How many MLB All-Star Games was Leo Cardenas named to in his 16-season MLB career?

    a. 2

    b. 3

    c. 5

    d. 6

19. How many times did Mickey Vernon win the American League batting title in his 20-season MLB career?

    a. 0

    b. 1

    c. 2

    d. 3

20. Roy Sievers was named to five MLB All-Star Games in his 17-season MLB career.

    a. True

    b. False

QUIZ ANSWERS

1. B – 1991

2. A- True

3. C – 18

4. B – 2

5. D – 1956

6. C – 3

7. A – True

8. B – 1

9. D – 7

10. B – 2006

11. D – 4

12. A – True

13. C – 1979

14. B – 1962

15. C – 2

16. A – True

17. D – 10

18. C – 5

19. C – 2

20. A – True

DID YOU KNOW?

1. Kent Hrbek spent his entire 14-season MLB career with the Minnesota Twins. He was a 1x MLB All-Star and 2x World Series champion.

2. Chuck Knoblauch spent 7 seasons of his 12-season MLB career with the Minnesota Twins. He also played for the New York Yankees and Kansas City Royals. He was an American League Rookie of the Year, 4x MLB All-Star, 4x World Series champion, Gold Glove Award winner, and 2x Silver Slugger Award winner.

3. David Ortiz spent 6 seasons of his 20-season MLB career with the Minnesota Twins. He also played for the Boston Red Sox. He was a 10x MLB All-Star, 3x World Series champion, 7x Silver Slugger Award winner, World Series MVP, and ALCS MVP.

4. Justin Morneau spent 11 seasons of his 14-season MLB career with the Minnesota Twins. He also played for the Colorado Rockies, Pittsburgh Pirates, and Chicago White Sox. He was an MVP, 4x MLB All-Star, 2x Silver Slugger Award winner, and batting title champion.

5. Gary Gaetti spent 10 seasons of his 20-season MLB career with the Minnesota Twins. He also played for the Kansas City Royals, California Angels, St. Louis Cardinals, Chicago Cubs, and Boston Red Sox. He was a 2x MLB All-

Star, World Series champion, 4x Gold Glove Award winner, Silver Slugger Award winner, and ALCS MVP.

6. Leo Cardenas spent 3 seasons of his 16-season MLB career with the Minnesota Twins. He also played for the Cincinnati Reds, Texas Rangers, Cleveland Indians, and California Angels. He was a 5x MLB All-Star and Gold Glove Award winner.

7. Brian Dozier spent seven seasons of his nine-season MLB career with the Minnesota Twins. He also played for the Washington Nationals, New York Mets, and Los Angeles Dodgers. He is a 1x MLB All-Star, Gold Glove Award winner, and World Series champion.

8. Zoilo Versalles spent 9 seasons of his 12-season MLB career with the Minnesota Twins. He also played for the Los Angeles Dodgers, Cleveland Indians, Washington Senators, and Atlanta Braves. He was an MVP, 2x MLB All-Star, and 2x Gold Glove Award winner.

9. Joe Cronin spent 7 seasons of his 20-season MLB career with the Washington Senators. He also played for the Boston Red Sox and Pittsburgh Pirates. He was a 7x MLB All-Star and is a member of the National Baseball Hall of Fame.

10. Mickey Vernon spent 14 seasons of his 20-season MLB career with the Washington Senators. He also played for the Cleveland Indians, Boston Red Sox, Pittsburgh Pirates, and Milwaukee Braves. He was a 7x MLB All-Star and 2x batting title champion.

CHAPTER 12:

PITCHERS AND CATCHERS

QUIZ TIME!

1. How many Silver Slugger Awards did Joe Mauer win in his 15-season MLB career?

    a. 3
    b. 4
    c. 5
    d. 6

2. Kurt Suzuki was named to his only MLB All-Star Game during his 2014 season with the Minnesota Twins.

    a. True
    b. False

3. Over the course of his 14-season MLB career, Terry Steinbach played for the Minnesota Twins and which other team?

    a. San Francisco Giants
    b. Los Angeles Dodgers

c. San Diego Padres

d. Oakland A's

4. How many Cy Young Awards did Johan Santana win?

    a. 1

    b. 2

    c. 3

    d. 4

5. How many Gold Glove Awards did Jim Kaat win in his 25-season MLB career?

    a. 10

    b. 12

    c. 14

    d. 16

6. How many MLB All-Star Games was Jim Perry named to in his 17-season MLB career?

    a. 1

    b. 2

    c. 3

    d. 4

7. Camilo Pascual was named to seven MLB All-Star Games in his 18-season MLB career.

    a. True

    b. False

8. What year was Walter Johnson inducted into the National Baseball Hall of Fame?

a. 1935

b. 1936

c. 1937

d. 1938

9. What year was Bert Blyleven inducted into the National Baseball Hall of Fame?

   a. 1995

   b. 1999

   c. 2007

   d. 2011

10. Frank Viola won his sole Cy Young Award during his _____ season with the Minnesota Twins.

    a. 1983

    b. 1986

    c. 1988

    d. 1989

11. How many MLB All-Star Games was Dutch Leonard named to in his 20-season MLB career?

    a. 1

    b. 2

    c. 4

    d. 5

12. Brad Radke spent his entire 12-season MLB career with the Minnesota Twins.

    a. True

    b. False

13. How many MLB All-Star Games was Joe Nathan named to in his 16-season MLB career?

    a. 8
    b. 6
    c. 5
    d. 2

14. How many seasons did Rick Aguilera spend with the Minnesota Twins?

    a. 9
    b. 10
    c. 11
    d. 12

15. How many Gold Glove Awards did Earl Battey win in his 13-season MLB career?

    a. 1
    b. 2
    c. 3
    d. 4

16. Glen Perkins spent his entire 12-season MLB career with the Minnesota Twins.

    a. True
    b. False

17. What year was Stan Coveleski inducted into the National Baseball Hall of Fame?

    a. 1968
    b. 1969

c. 1970

d. 1971

18. As of the end of the 2020 season, how many MLB All-Star Games has current Twins pitcher Jose Berríos been named to?

a. 0

b. 1

c. 2

d. 3

19. How many seasons did Francisco Liriano spend with the Minnesota Twins?

a. 4

b. 5

c. 6

d. 7

20. Firpo Marberry spent 11 seasons of his 14 season MLB career with the Washington Senators.

a. True

b. False

QUIZ ANSWERS

1. C – 5

2. A – True

3. D – Oakland A's

4. B – 2

5. D – 16

6. C – 3

7. A – True

8. B – 1936

9. D – 2011

10. C – 1988

11. D – 5

12. A – True

13. B – 6

14. C – 11

15. C – 3

16. A – True

17. B – 1969

18. C – 2

19. D – 7

20. A – True

DID YOU KNOW?

1. Joe Mauer spent his entire 15-season MLB career with the Minnesota Twins. He was an MVP, 6x MLB All-Star, 3x Gold Glove Award winner, 5x Silver Slugger Award winner, and 3x Batting title champion.

2. Terry Steinbach spent 3 seasons of his 14-season MLB career with the Minnesota Twins. He also played for the Oakland A's. He was a 3x MLB All-Star, All-Star MVP, and World Series champion.

3. Kurt Suzuki spent 3 seasons of his MLB career with the Minnesota Twins. He currently plays for the Los Angeles Angels. He has also played for the Oakland A's, Washington Nationals, and Atlanta Braves. He is a 1x MLB All-Star and World Series champion.

4. Walter Johnson spent his entire 21-season MLB career with the Washington Senators. He was a member of the National Baseball Hall of Fame, 2x MVP, 3x Triple Crown winner, World Series champion, and 5x ERA title champion.

5. Jim Kaat spent 15 seasons of his 25-season MLB career with the Minnesota Twins/Washington Senators. He also played for the Philadelphia Phillies, St. Louis Cardinals, Chicago White Sox, and New York Yankees. He was a 16x

Gold Glove Award winner, 3x MLB All-Star, and World Series champion.

6. Johan Santana spent 8 seasons of his 12-season MLB career with the Minnesota Twins. He also played for the New York Mets. He was a 2x Cy Young Award winner, Triple Crown winner, 4x MLB All-Star, Gold Glove Award winner, and 3x ERA title champion.

7. Frank Viola spent 8 seasons of his 15-season MLB career with the Minnesota Twins. He also played for the New York Mets, Boston Red Sox, Cincinnati Reds, and Toronto Blue Jays. He was a 3x MLB All-Star, Cy Young Award winner, World Series champion, and World Series MVP.

8. Jim Perry spent 10 seasons of his 17-season MLB career with the Minnesota Twins. He also played for the Oakland A's, Cleveland Indians, and Detroit Tigers. He was a 3x MLB All-Star and Cy Young Award winner.

9. Bert Blyleven spent 11 seasons of his 22-season MLB career with the Minnesota Twins. He also played for the Cleveland Indians, Pittsburgh Pirates, California Angels, and Texas Rangers. He was a member of the National Baseball Hall of Fame, 2x MLB All-Star, and 2x World Series champion.

10. Camilo Pascual spent 13 seasons of his 18-season MLB career with the Minnesota Twins/Washington Senators. He also played for the Washington Senators, Los Angeles Dodgers, Cleveland Indians, and Cincinnati Reds. He was a 7x MLB All-Star.

CHAPTER 13:

WORLD SERIES

QUIZ TIME!

1. How many World Series championships have the Minnesota Twins won?

   a. 1
   b. 2
   c. 3
   d. 4

2. How many AL pennants have the Minnesota Twins?

   a. 5
   b. 6
   c. 8
   d. 9

3. Which team did the Washington Senators face in the 1924 World Series?

   a. Brooklyn Robins
   b. Pittsburgh Pirates

c. New York Giants

d. St. Louis Cardinals

4. Which team did the Washington Senators face in the 1925 World Series?

   a. Boston Braves

   b. Cincinnati Reds

   c. New York Giants

   d. Pittsburgh Pirates

5. Which team did the Washington Senators face in the 1933 World Series?

   a. New York Giants

   b. Brooklyn Dodgers

   c. Philadelphia Phillies

   d. Pittsburgh Pirates

6. Which team did the Minnesota Twins face in the 1965 World Series?

   a. San Francisco Giants

   b. Cincinnati Reds

   c. Los Angeles Dodgers

   d. Pittsburgh Pirates

7. The Minnesota Twins faced the St. Louis Cardinals in the 1987 World Series.

   a. True

   b. False

8. Which team did the Minnesota Twins face in the 1991 World Series?

    a. Cincinnati Reds
    b. Atlanta Braves
    c. Houston Astros
    d. Montreal Expos

9. What year did the Minnesota Twins win their only wild card?

    a. 2001
    b. 2008
    c. 2013
    d. 2017

10. How many games did the 1924 World Series go?

    a. 4
    b. 5
    c. 6
    d. 7

11. How many games did the 1925 World Series go?

    a. 4
    b. 5
    c. 6
    d. 7

12. The 1933 World Series went 5 games.

    a. True
    b. False

13. How many games did the 1965 World Series go?

    a. 4
    b. 5
    c. 6
    d. 7

14. How many games did the 1987 World Series go?

    a. 4
    b. 5
    c. 6
    d. 7

15. How many games did the 1991 World Series go?

    a. 4
    b. 5
    c. 6
    d. 7

16. The Minnesota Twins hold the record for the longest losing streak in the postseason out of all four major North American professional sports. The Twins have lost 18 consecutive playoff games since 2004.

    a. True
    b. False

17. Who was the manager of the Washington Senators during the 1924 and 1925 World Series?

    a. Donie Bush
    b. Bucky Harris

c. Walter Johnson

d. Joe Cronin

18. Who was the manager of the Washington Senators during the 1933 World Series?

    a. Bucky Harris

    b. Ossie Bluege

    c. Joe Cronin

    d. Chuck Dressen

19. Who was the manager of the Minnesota Twins during the 1965 World Series?

    a. Cal Ermer

    b. Sam Mele

    c. Cookie Lavagetto

    d. Bill Rigney

20. Tom Kelly was manager of the Minnesota Twins during the 1987 and 1991 World Series.

    a. True

    b. False

QUIZ ANSWERS

1. C – 3 (1924,1987,1991)

2. B – 6 (1924, 1925, 1933, 1965, 1987, 1991)

3. C – New York Giants

4. D – Pittsburgh Pirates

5. A – New York Giants

6. C – Los Angeles Dodgers

7. A – True

8. B – Atlanta Braves

9. D – 2017

10. D – 7

11. D – 7

12. A - True

13. D – 7

14. D – 7

15. D – 7

16. A – True

17. B – Bucky Harris

18. C – Joe Cronin

19. B – Sam Mele

20. A – True

DID YOU KNOW?

1. The 1991 World Series was unique because both the Minnesota Twins and Atlanta Braves had finished in last place the previous season.

2. 1987 was the first World Series to feature games played indoors. It was also the first in which the home team won every game.

3. In 1965, Sandy Koufax did not pitch in Game 1 of the World Series because it was Yom Kippur, and he is Jewish.

4. The 1933 World Series was the last played in Washington, DC, until 2019. The Washington Nationals would go on to win the 2019 World Series.

5. The 1924 World Series was the first World Series to use the 2–3–2 pattern. This means two games were played in a row at one stadium, then three at the other, then the last two went back to the first stadium.

6. 1924 was the Washington Senators' only World Series championship victory until the franchise moved to Minnesota.

7. The 1924 World Series took place from October 4 through October 10; the 1925 World Series took place from October 7 through October 15; the 1933 World Series took place from October 3 through October 7; the 1965 World Series took place from October 6 through October 14; the 1979

World Series took place from October 17 through October 25; the 1991 World Series took place from October 19 through October 27.

8. The 1987 World Series MVP was Frank Viola. The 1991 World Series MVP was Jack Morris.

9. ESPN named the 1924 World Series the third greatest World Series of all time.

10. The 1991 World Series is Minnesota's most recent World Series championship and its most recent appearance in a World Series.

CHAPTER 14:

HEATED RIVALRIES

QUIZ TIME!

1. Which team does NOT play in the American League Central with the Minnesota Twins?

    a. Chicago White Sox

    b. St. Louis Cardinals

    c. Cleveland Indians

    d. Detroit Tigers

2. The Minnesota Twins were in the American League West Division from 1969-1993.

    a. True

    b. False

3. Which team was once a member of the AL Central Division?

    a. Chicago Cubs

    b. Milwaukee Brewers

    c. St. Louis Cardinals

    d. Pittsburgh Pirates

4. What current American League Central team has the most AL Central championships?

    a. Detroit Tigers
    b. Minnesota Twins
    c. Cleveland Indians
    d. Kansas City Royals

5. The Chicago White Sox and Kansas City Royals are the only teams from the American League Central to have won the World Series since the realignment in 1994.

    a. True
    b. False

6. Which team won the American League Central in 2020?

    a. Kansas City Royals
    b. Chicago White Sox
    c. Detroit Tigers
    d. Minnesota Twins

7. Each team in the American League Central has won at least two World Series championships.

    a. True
    b. False

8. The Twins have three World Series championships. How many do the Chicago White Sox have?

    a. 0
    b. 1
    c. 2
    d. 3

9. The Twins have three World Series championships. How many do the Cleveland Indians have?

   a. 0
   b. 1
   c. 2
   d. 3

10. The Twins have three World Series championships. How many do the Detroit Tigers have?

   a. 1
   b. 2
   c. 3
   d. 4

11. The Twins have three World Series championships. How many do the Kansas City Royals have?

   a. 1
   b. 2
   c. 3
   d. 4

12. The Minnesota Twins have NOT conducted a trade with the Chicago White Sox since.

   a. True
   b. False

13. Which player has NOT played for both the Twins and the Chicago White Sox?

   a. Earl Battey
   b. Jim Kaat

c. Bert Blyleven
d. Justin Morneau

14. Which player has NOT played for both the Twins and the Cleveland Indians?

    a. Bert Blyleven
    b. Camilo Pascual
    c. Jim Perry
    d. Chuck Knoblauch

15. Which player has NOT played for both the Twins and the Detroit Tigers?

    a. Goose Goslin
    b. Bob Allison
    c. Joe Nathan
    d. Delmon Young

16. The American League Central Division was founded in 1994.

    a. True
    b. False

17. Which player has NOT played for both the Twins and the Kansas City Royals?

    a. Torii Hunter
    b. Gary Gaetti
    c. Harmon Killebrew
    d. Ervin Santana

18. Which player has NOT played for both the Twins and the Milwaukee Brewers?

    a. J.J. Hardy
    b. Carlos Gomez
    c. Tom Brunansky
    d. Brad Radke

19. How many AL Central Division titles did the Milwaukee Brewers win before they moved to the NL Central?

    a. 0
    b. 1
    c. 3
    d. 4

20. The Minnesota Twins won 4 AL West Division championships before they moved to the AL Central.

    a. True
    b. False

QUIZ ANSWERS

1. B – St. Louis Cardinals

2. A – True

3. B – Milwaukee Brewers

4. C – Cleveland Indians (10)

5. A – True

6. D – Minnesota Twins

7. A – True

8. D – 3

9. C – 2

10. D – 4

11. B – 2

12. A – True

13. C – Bert Blyleven

14. D – Chuck Knoblauch

15. B – Bob Allison

16. A- True

17. A – Torii Hunter

18. D – Brad Radke

19. A – 0

20. A – True

DID YOU KNOW?

1. The Cleveland Indians have the most American League Central Division championships with. The Minnesota Twins have eight, the Detroit Tigers have four, the Chicago White Sox have three, and the Kansas City Royals have one. The Milwaukee Brewers, formerly of the AL Central, did not win a division title during their time in the AL Central. The Minnesota Twins won four AL West championships (1969, 1970, 1987, 1991). The most recent AL Central Division champions are the Minnesota Twins (2020). The Twins won the AL Central in 2002-2004, 2006, 2009, 2010, and 2019–2020.

2. When the AL Central was founded, the Chicago White Sox, Kansas City Royals, and Minnesota Twins moved in from the AL West. The Cleveland Indians and Milwaukee Brewers moved in from the AL East. In 1997, the Detroit Tigers moved in from the AL East.

3. All teams in the American League Central are located in the Midwestern United States.

4. In 1997, with the debut of the Tampa Bay Devil Rays in the AL East, the Detroit Tigers moved to the AL Central. The Brewers then moved to the NL Central to give each division an even number of teams.

5. The American League Central is one of two divisions in which every team has won at least one World Series championship.

6. Bert Blyleven, Orlando Cabrera, Leo Cardenas, Jamey Carroll, Dean Chance, Tyler Clippard, Alex Cole, Bartolo Colón, Stan Coveleski, Rick Dempsey, Mudcat Grant, Jimmie Hall, Rich Hill, Jim Lemon, Joe Lis, Billy Martin, Terry Mulholland, Gregg Olson, Camilo Pascual, Jim Perry, Roger Peckinpaugh, Sam Rice, Jim Thome, Mickey Vernon, Dave Winfield, and Zoilo Versalles have all played for both the Minnesota Twins and the Cleveland Indians.

7. Alex Avila, Doc Ayers, Billy Beane, Dave Boswell, Dean Chance, Dan Gladden, Goose Goslin, Whitey Herzog, Torii Hunter, Jacque Jones, Francisco Liriano, Firpo Mayberry, Billy Martin, Joe Nathan, Jim Nettles, Gregg Olsen, Jim Perry, Fernando Rodney, Mark Salas, Eddie Yost, and Delmon Young have all played for both the Minnesota Twins and the Detroit Tigers.

8. Gerry Arrigo, Earl Battey, Orlando Cabrera, Tyler Clippard, Bartolo Colón, Sam Dente, Orlando Hudson, Philip Humber, Jim Kaat, Pat Kelly, Jim Lemon, Francisco Liriano, Mike McCormick, Justin Morneau, Roger Peckinpaugh, A.J. Pierzynski, Ervin Santana, Roy Sievers, Eric Soderholm, Roy Smalley, Kevin Tapani, Jim Thome, and Early Wynn have all played for both the Minnesota Twins and the Chicago White Sox.

9. Paul Abbott, Homer Bailey, Steve Braun, Drew Butera, Jamey Carroll, Chili Davis, Gary Gaetti, Greg Gagne, Liam Hendriks, Pat Kelly, Harmon Killebrew, Chuck Knoblauch, Shane Mack, Doug Mientkiewicz, Kendrys Morales, Jim Nettles, Gregg Olson, Ervin Santana, Danny Valencia, and Josh Willingham have all played for both the Minnesota Twins and the Kansas City Royals.

10. Grant Balfour, Tom Brunansky, Jeff Cirillo, Nelson Cruz, Rick Dempsey, Matt Garza, Carlos Gomez, J.J. Hardy, LaTroy Hawkins, Larry Hisle, Kyle Lohse, Logan Morrison, and Jonathan Schoop have all played for both the Minnesota Twins and the Milwaukee Brewers.

CHAPTER 15:

THE AWARDS SECTION

QUIZ TIME!

1. Which Washington Senators player won the American League MVP Award in 1913 and 1924?

    a. Ossie Bluege

    b. Joe Judge

    c. Walter Johnson

    d. Clyde Milan

2. Kirby Puckett is the only Minnesota Twins player to ever win the All-Star Game MVP Award.

    a. True

    b. False

3. How many Cy Young Awards did Johan Santana win during his time with the Minnesota Twins?

    a. 0

    b. 1

    c. 2

    d. 3

4. Which Minnesota Twins player most recently won the American League Rookie of the Year?

   a. Rod Carew
   b. Chuck Knoblauch
   c. Brian Dozier
   d. Marty Cordova

5. Which Minnesota Twins pitcher won the 2009 American League Rolaids Relief Award?

   a. Matt Guerrier
   b. Joe Nathan
   c. Jose Mijares
   d. Bobby Keppel

6. Which Minnesota Twins player won a Silver Slugger Award in 2012?

   a. Brian Dozier
   b. Denard Span
   c. Josh Willingham
   d. Justin Morneau

7. No Minnesota Twins player has ever won the MLB Home Run Derby.

   a. True
   b. False

8. Which Minnesota Twins player was named the DHL Hometown Hero (Voted by MLB fans as the most outstanding player in franchise history)?

a. Joe Mauer

b. Rod Carew

c. Harmon Killebrew

d. Kirby Puckett

9. Who was the first Minnesota Twins player to win an American League Gold Glove Award?

a. Jim Kaat

b. Earl Battey

c. Zoilo Versalles

d. Tony Oliva

10. Who was the first Minnesota Twins player to win a Silver Slugger Award?

a. Paul Molitor

b. Chuck Knoblauch

c. Kirby Puckett

d. Harmon Killebrew

11. Which Minnesota Twins pitcher is the only in franchise history to win an MLB/AL Pitching Triple Crown?

a. Johan Santana

b. Jim Perry

c. Glen Perkins

d. Brad Radke

12. No Minnesota Twins third baseman, OR shortstop, has won a Silver Slugger Award.

a. True

b. False

13. Tony Oliva was named the American League Rookie of the Year in which year?

    a. 1961
    b. 1963
    c. 1964
    d. 1965

14. How many consecutive Silver Slugger Awards did Joe Mauer win during his career with the Minnesota Twins?

    a. 2
    b. 3
    c. 4
    d. 5

15. Torii Hunter won consecutive American League Gold Glove Awards with the Minnesota Twins from 2001 through which year?

    a. 2004
    b. 2005
    c. 2006
    d. 2007

16. Ron Gardenhire was named the 2010 American League Manager of the Year.

    a. True
    b. False

17. Which Minnesota Twins player won the 1988 American League Cy Young Award?

a. Joe Niekro

b. Bert Blyleven

c. Tippy Martinez

d. Frank Viola

18. Which Minnesota Twins player won a Silver Slugger Award in 2019?

a. Mitch Garver

b. Nelson Cruz

c. Max Kepler

d. Both A and B

19. Which Washington Senators player was named the 1925 American League MVP?

a. Ossie Bluege

b. Roger Peckinpaugh

c. Sam Rice

d. Goose Goslin

20. The Minnesota Twins as a team won the 2012 and 2013 Wilson Defensive Team of the Year Award.

a. True

b. False

QUIZ ANSWERS

1. C – Walter Johnson

2. A – True

3. C – 2

4. D – Marty Cordova (1995)

5. B – Joe Nathan

6. C – Josh Willingham

7. B – False, Justin Morneau (2008)

8. D – Kirby Puckett

9. B – Earl Battey (1960)

10. C – Kirby Puckett (1986)

11. A – Johan Santana (2006)

12. A- True

13. C – 1964

14. C – 4 (2006 through 2010)

15. D – 2007

16. A – True

17. D – Frank Viola

18. D – Both A and B

19. B – Roger Peckinpaugh

20. A – True

DID YOU KNOW?

1. The Minnesota Twins have had three different pitchers win American League Cy Young Awards, Jim Perry (1970), Frank Viola (1988), and Johan Santana (2004 and 2006).

2. The Minnesota Twins have had eight different players win Silver Slugger Awards, Paul Molitor, Nelson Cruz, Joe Mauer, Mitch Garver, Justin Morneau, Chuck Knoblauch, Kirby Puckett, and Josh Willingham.

3. The Minnesota Twins have had seven different players named American League Rookie of the Year, Albie Pearson (1958), Bob Allison (1959), Tony Oliva (1964), Rod Carew (1967), John Castino (1979), Chuck Knoblauch (1991), and Marty Cordova (1995).

4. The Minnesota Twins have had 14 different players win American League Gold Glove Awards, Jim Kaat, Johan Santana, Earl Battey, Joe Mauer, Vic Power, Doug Mientkiewicz, Brian Dozier, Chuck Knoblauch, Gary Gaetti, Zoilo Versalles, Bryan Buxton, Torii Hunter, Kirby Puckett, and Tony Oliva.

5. The Minnesota Twins have had seven different players win the American League MVP Award:,Walter Johnson (1913 and 1924), Roger Peckinpaugh (1925), Zoilo Versalles

(1965), Harmon Killebrew (1969), Rod Carew (1977), Justin Morneau (2006), and Joe Mauer (2009).

6. The Minnesota Twins have had two different players win the American League Rolaids Relief Man of the Year Award, Bill Campbell (1976) and Joe Nathan (2009).

7. The Minnesota Twins have had only one player win the MLB All-Star Game MVP Award, Kirby Puckett in 1993.

8. Joe Mauer was named the 2009 Baseball America Major League Player of the Year.

9. The Minnesota Twins have had four different managers win the American League Manager of the Year Award, Tom Kelly (1991), Ron Gardenhire (2010), Paul Molitor (2017), and Rocco Baldelli (2019).

10. Ron Gardenhire was named the 2008 Baseball America Manager of the Year.

CHAPTER 16:

THE LAND OF 10,000 LAKES

QUIZ TIME!

1. How many square feet is the Mall of America in Bloomington, Minnesota?

   a. 8 million
   b. 9 million
   c. 9.5 million
   d. 10 million

2. The Metrodome in Minneapolis is the only stadium in the United States to have hosted a World Series, a Super Bowl, and an NCAA Final Four Basketball championship.

   a. True
   b. False

3. Which celebrity is NOT from Minnesota?

   a. Judy Garland
   b. Jessica Biel
   c. Prince
   d. Beyonce

4. Which theater in Minneapolis is the largest regional playhouse in the United States?

   a. Swan

   b. Globe

   c. Guthrie

   d. Red Lion

5. Minneapolis has more of what per capita, than any other city in the United States?

   a. Bars

   b. Golfers

   c. Cars

   d. Dogs

6. Which famous candy bar was invented in Minneapolis?

   a. Milky Way

   b. Snickers

   c. Reese's Peanut Butter Cups

   d. Both A and B

7. Minnesota produces more turkeys each year than there are people in California.

   a. True

   b. False

8. What is the name of Minnesota's NFL team?

   a. Minnesota 49ers

   b. Minnesota Rams

   c. Minnesota Dolphins

   d. Minnesota Vikings

9. What is the name of Minnesota's MLS team?

   a. Minnesota Earthquakes
   b. Minnesota Galaxy
   c. Minnesota United FC
   d. Sporting Minnesota

10. What is the name of Minnesota's NBA team?

   a. Minnesota Warriors
   b. Minnesota Timberwolves
   c. Minnesota Mavericks
   d. Minnesota Thunder

11. What is the name of the Minnesota Vikings' current stadium?

   a. M&T Bank Stadium
   b. U.S. Bank Stadium
   c. Arrowhead Stadium
   d. State Farm Stadium

12. Minnesota's NHL team is called the Minnesota Wild.

   a. True
   b. False

13. What is the name of the Minnesota Wild's current arena?

   a. T-Mobile Arena
   b. SAP Center
   c. Bridgestone Arena
   d. Xcel Energy Center

14. Minnesota United FC's home stadium is Allianz Field.

a. True

b. False

15. What is the name of the Minnesota Timberwolves' current arena?

    a. Amway Center

    b. Chase Center

    c. Target Center

    d. United Center

16. The Minneapolis Skyway, an indoor pedestrian walkway system that links seven miles of downtown buildings, is the longest continuous skyway system in the world.

    a. True

    b. False

17. Which city is the capital of Minnesota?

    a. Bloomington

    b. St. Paul

    c. Minneapolis

    d. Duluth

18. What is Minneapolis-St. Paul International Airport's code?

    a. MIA

    b. SPI

    c. SPM

    d. MSP

19. As of 2011, nearly what percentage of adults in Minneapolis and St. Paul devoted some of their free time to volunteer work?

    a. 10

    b. 20

    c. 30

    d. 40

20. Minneapolis is America's "Most Literate City."

    a. True

    b. False

QUIZ ANSWERS

1. C – 9.5 million

2. A - True

3. D – Beyonce

4. C – Guthrie

5. B – Golfers

6. D – Both A and B

7. A- True

8. D – Minnesota Vikings

9. C – Minnesota United FC

10. B – Minnesota Timberwolves

11. B – U.S. Bank Stadium

12. A- True

13. D – Xcel Energy Arena

14. A – True

15. C – Target Center

16. A – True

17. B – St. Paul

18. D – MSP

19. D – 40

20. A – True

DID YOU KNOW?

1. In 2012, the Walker Art Center in Minneapolis hosted the world's first Internet Cat Video Festival.

2. Minnesota has no sales tax on apparel and accessories.

3. The *Mary Tyler Moore Show,* a 1970s sitcom, followed the life of a 30-year-old woman as she adjusted to life on her own in Minneapolis, after a bad break-up.

4. The Honeycrisp apple was invented by the University of Minnesota as part of an apple breeding program.

5. Target, Best Buy, General Mills, and Land O'Lakes call Minnesota home.

6. *Peanuts* creator Charles Shulz was born in Minneapolis and grew up in St. Paul.

7. Almost 10,000 cyclists are on the roads, paths, and trails of Minneapolis every day.

8. Minneapolis native Marjorie Husted created the Betty Crocker cooking and baking character in 1921. The Pillsbury Company is based in Minneapolis.

9. Cheerleading was invented in 1898 at the University of Minnesota.

10. Minneapolis is the *Guinness Book of World Records* record holder for the "Quietest Place on Earth."

CHAPTER 17:

KILLER

QUIZ TIME!

1. What is Harmon Killebrew's full name?

    a. Harmon Christopher Killebrew

    b. Harmon Charles Killebrew

    c. Harmon Calvin Killebrew

    d. Harmon Clayton Killebrew

2. Harmon Killebrew played his entire 22-season MLB career with the Washington Senators/Minnesota Twins.

    a. True

    b. False

3. Where was Harmon Killebrew born?

    a. Muncie, Indiana

    b. Carmel, Indiana

    c. Payette, Idaho

    d. Boise, Idaho

4. When was Harmon Killebrew born?

a. June 29, 1933

b. June 29, 1936

c. July 29, 1933

d. July 29, 1936

5. Harmon Killebrew was named the 1969 American League MVP.

   a. True

   b. False

6. How many Gold Glove Awards did Harmon Killebrew win?

   a. 0

   b. 1

   c. 2

   d. 3

7. What year was Harmon Killebrew inducted into the National Baseball Hall of Fame with 83.1% of the vote?

   a. 1982

   b. 1983

   c. 1984

   d. 1985

8. After retiring from baseball, Harmon Killebrew became a television broadcaster for several baseball teams from 1976 to 1988.

   a. True

   b. False

9. How many World Series championships did Harmon Killebrew win?

   a. 0
   b. 1
   c. 2
   d. 3

10. What year did Harmon Killebrew make his MLB debut?

   a. 1953
   b. 1954
   c. 1955
   d. 1958

11. How many MLB All-Star Games was Harmon Killebrew named to?

   a. 11
   b. 12
   c. 13
   d. 15

12. The Minnesota Twins retired Harmon Killebrew's No. 3 on May 4, 1975.

   a. True
   b. False

13. Harmon Killebrew was inducted into the Minnesota Twins Hall of Fame in _____.

   a. 2000
   b. 2001

c. 2002

d. 2003

14. Harmon Killebrew hit 573 home runs.

  a. True

  b. False

15. How many RBIs did Harmon Killebrew collect?

  a. 1,384

  b. 1,484

  c. 1,584

  d. 1,684

16. What is Harmon Killebrew's career batting average?

  a. .246

  b. .256

  c. .266

  d. .276

17. Harmon Killebrew was the American League home run leader six times.

  a. True

  b. False

18. How many times was Harmon Killebrew the American League RBI leader?

  a. 1

  b. 2

  c. 3

  d. 4

19. How many bases did Harmon Killebrew steal?

    a. 19
    b. 49
    c. 79
    d. 109

20. Harmon Killebrew attended Albertson College in Caldwell, Idaho.

    a. True
    b. False

QUIZ ANSWERS

1. D – Harmon Clayton Killebrew

2. B – False (He spent one season with the Kansas City Royals.)

3. C – Payette, Idaho

4. B – June 29, 1936

5. A – True

6. A – 0

7. C – 1984

8. A – True

9. A – 0

10. B – 1954

11. C – 13

12. A – True

13. A – 2000

14. A – True

15. C – 1,584

16. B - .256

17. A – True

18. C – 3

19. A – 19

20. A – True

DID YOU KNOW?

1. Once, when asked what hobbies he had, Harmon Killebrew replied, "Just washing the dishes, I guess."

2. After retiring as a player, Harmon Killebrew served as a hitting instructor for the Oakland Athletics.

3. At the time of his retirement, Harmon Killebrew had the fourth-most home runs in MLB history. He has the second-most home runs in the American League, second to only the legendary Babe Ruth. He was also the American League career leader in home runs by a right-handed batter.

4. Harmon Killebrew hit the longest measured home runs at Minnesota's Metropolitan Stadium (520 feet) and at Baltimore's Memorial Stadium (471 feet).

5. For the Twins' first year in Minnesota, Harmon Killebrew was named team captain by manager Cookie Lavagetto.

6. "If Harmon Killebrew isn't the league's best player, I've never seen one." – Reggie Jackson

7. The street along the south side of the Mall of America, the former site of Metropolitan Stadium, in Bloomington, Minnesota, was named "Killebrew Drive" in honor of Harmon Killebrew.

8. Many believe that Harmon Killebrew was the player depicted in the Major League Baseball logo. The creator of said logo claims that the logo was not based on any player at all. However, Killebrew is the model for the Major League Baseball Players Alumni Association logo.

9. The Harmon Killebrew Foundation has helped fundraise for Vista Hospice Care, The Gillette Children's Miracle Network, Healing Hands for Haiti, and the Miracle Leagues of Minnesota, Arizona, and other states.

10. "No individual has ever meant more to the Minnesota Twins organization and millions of fans across Twins Territory than Harmon Killebrew. Harmon will long be remembered as one of the most prolific home run hitters in the history of the game and the leader of a group of players who helped lay the foundation for the long-term success of the Twins franchise and Major League Baseball in the Upper Midwest. However, more important, Harmon's legacy will be the class, dignity, and humility he demonstrated each and every day as a Hall of Fame-quality husband, father, friend, teammate, and man." — Twins' President Dave St. Peter in the *Star Tribune* following Killebrew's death

CHAPTER 18:

PUCK

QUIZ TIME!

1. Where was Kirby Puckett born?

    a. Naperville, Illinois

    b. Oswego, Illinois

    c. Chicago, Illinois

    d. Peoria, Illinois

2. Kirby Puckett was the fourth baseball player during the 1900s to record 1,000 hits in his first five full years in the MLB and the second to record 2,000 hits during his first ten full years in the MLB.

    a. True

    b. False

3. How many Silver Slugger Awards did Kirby Puckett win?

    a. 1

    b. 3

    c. 5

    d. 6

4. How many Gold Glove Awards did Kirby Puckett win?

    a. 8

    b. 6

    c. 4

    d. 3

5. How many MLB All-Star Games was Kirby Puckett named to?

    a. 3

    b. 4

    c. 8

    d. 10

6. What year was Kirby Puckett inducted into the National Baseball Hall of Fame with 82.1% of the vote?

    a. 2001

    b. 2003

    c. 2005

    d. 2007

7. Kirby Puckett played his entire 12-season MLB career with the Minnesota Twins.

    a. True

    b. False

8. What year did the Minnesota Twins retire Kirby Puckett's No. 34?

    a. 1995

    b. 1996

c. 1997

d. 2001

9. What year was Kirby Puckett inducted into the Minnesota Twins Hall of Fame?

    a. 2000

    b. 2001

    c. 2002

    d. 2003

10. What year was Kirby Puckett named the ALCS MVP?

    a. 1985

    b. 1989

    c. 1990

    d. 1991

11. What was Kirby Puckett's career batting average?

    a. .298

    b. .308

    c. .318

    d. .328

12. Kirby Puckett was named the 1993 All-Star Game MVP.

    a. True

    b. False

13. How many home runs did Kirby Puckett hit?

    a. 107

    b. 207

    c. 307

    d. 407

14. How many RBIs did Kirby Puckett collect?

   a. 885

   b. 985

   c. 1,085

   d. 1,185

15. How many hits did Kirby Puckett collect?

   a. 2,204

   b. 2,304

   c. 2,404

   d. 2,504

16. Kirby Puckett did NOT win a World Series championship in his 12-season MLB career.

   a. True

   b. False

17. Kirby Puckett was the American League batting champion in which year?

   a. 1985

   b. 1987

   c. 1989

   d. 1991

18. Kirby Puckett was the American League RBI leader in which year?

   a. 1989

   b. 1990

   c. 1992

   d. 1994

19. Kirby Puckett died in which year, following a massive hemorrhagic stroke?

    a. 2005

    b. 2006

    c. 2007

    d. 2008

20. March 12 is "Kirby Puckett Day" in Minneapolis.

    a. True

    b. False

QUIZ ANSWERS

1. C – Chicago, Illinois

2. A – True

3. D – 6

4. B – 6

5. D – 10

6. A – 2001

7. A – True

8. C – 1997

9. A – 2000

10. D – 1991

11. C - .318

12. A – True

13. B – 207

14. C – 1,085

15. B – 2,304

16. B – False, 2 (1987, 1991)

17. C – 1989

18. D – 1994

19. B – 2006

20. A – True

DID YOU KNOW?

1. On April 12, 2010, a statue of Kirby Puckett was unveiled at the plaza of Target Field in Minneapolis. It is near Gate 34, numbered in honor of Puckett. The statue shows Puckett pumping his fist while running the bases, as he did after his winning home run in Game 6 of the 1991 World Series.

2. Upon his retirement in 2016, former Twins first baseman and designated hitter David Ortiz said that he had used the No. 34, with the Red Sox to honor his friendship with Kirby Puckett.

3. In 1993, Kirby Puckett received the Branch Rickey Award for his lifetime of community service work. He also was awarded the 1996 Roberto Clemente Award for community service.

4. At the time of his retirement, Kirby Puckett's .318 career batting average was the highest by any right-handed American League batter since Joe DiMaggio.

5. Kirby Puckett is the Minnesota Twins' all-time leader in career hits, runs, and total bases.

6. Kirby Puckett was forced to retire from baseball at age 36 due to glaucoma. When it was clear that he would never be able to play again, the Twins made him an executive vice-president of the team.

7. Kirby Puckett died at the second-youngest age, behind Lou Gehrig, of any Hall of Famer inducted while living. He was the youngest to die after being inducted in the era of the five-season waiting period.

8. A public memorial ceremony for Kirby Puckett at the Metrodome was attended by family, friends, players, and approximately 15,000 fans, even though there was an impending blizzard. Speakers at the service included Hall of Famers Harmon Killebrew, Cal Ripken Jr., and Dave Winfield, among many former teammates and coaches.

9. After receiving no scholarship offers following high school graduation, Kirby Puckett decided to work on an assembly line for Ford Motor Company. However, he was given the opportunity to attend Bradley University and after one year transferred to Triton College.

10. Kirby Puckett's MLB debut came on May 8, 1984, against the California Angels, a game in which he went 4 for 5 and scored one run.

CHAPTER 19:

AMERICA'S PASTIME

QUIZ TIME!

1. How many teams play in Major League Baseball?

    a. 15
    b. 20
    c. 30
    d. 33

2. Major League Baseball was founded in 1903.

    a. True
    b. False

3. Who is the current commissioner of Major League Baseball?

    a. Bart Giamatti
    b. Fay Vincent
    c. Bud Selig
    d. Rob Manfred

4. What year was the National League founded?

a. 1870

b. 1876

c. 1903

d. 1911

5. What year was the American League founded?

   a. 1888

   b. 1901

   c. 1903

   d. 1918

6. Major League Baseball is the second wealthiest professional sports league. Which league is the wealthiest?

   a. NBA

   b. NHL

   c. NFL

   d. MLS

7. The Major League Baseball headquarters is located in New York City.

   a. True

   b. False

8. How many games does each Major League Baseball team play per season?

   a. 92

   b. 122

   c. 162

   d. 192

9. In which two U.S. states is Major League Baseball's spring training held?

    a. California and Florida
    b. Arizona and Florida
    c. Arizona and California
    d. California and Arizona

10. How many stitches does an MLB baseball have?

    a. 98
    b. 100
    c. 108
    d. 110

11. Where is the National Baseball Hall of Fame located?

    a. Denver, Colorado
    b. Phoenix, Arizona
    c. Los Angeles, California
    d. Cooperstown, New York

12. All 30 Major League Baseball teams are located in the United States.

    a. True
    b. False

13. Which current Major League Baseball stadium is the oldest still in use?

    a. Angel Stadium
    b. Dodger Stadium
    c. Fenway Park
    d. Wrigley Field

14. Major League Baseball has the highest attendance of any sports league in the world.

    a. True
    b. False

15. Fill in the blank: Seventh Inning _____

    a. Jog
    b. Song
    c. Shake
    d. Stretch

16. William Howard Taft was the first U. S. President to throw out the ceremonial first pitch at a Major League Baseball game.

    a. True
    b. False

17. It is a Major League Baseball rule that all umpires must wear what colour underwear in case they rip their pants?

    a. Tan
    b. Gray
    c. White
    d. Black

18. What year was the first Baseball World Series played?

    a. 1903
    b. 1905
    c. 1915
    d. 1920

19. Former Major League Baseball Commissioner Bart Giamatti is the father of actor Paul Giamatti.

   a. True
   b. False

20. The song traditionally played in the middle of the seventh inning at Major League Baseball games is called *Take Me Out to the Ballpark*.

   a. True
   b. False

QUIZ ANSWERS

1. C – 30

2. A - True

3. D – Rob Manfred

4. B – 1876

5. B – 1901

6. C – NFL

7. A- True

8. C – 162

9. B – Arizona and Florida

10. C – 108

11. D – Cooperstown, New York

12. B – False (The Toronto Blue Jays are located in Canada.)

13. C – Fenway Park

14. A – True

15. D – Stretch

16. A – True

17. D – Black

18. A - 1903

19. A – True

20. B – False (It's *Take Me Out to the Ballgame*.)

DID YOU KNOW?

1. The average lifespan of a baseball in a Major League Baseball game is 5-7 pitches. This means approximately 5-6 dozen baseballs are used in every game.

2. The Boston Americans won the very first World Series. They defeated the Pittsburgh Pirates in 8 games. Today the most games a World Series can go is 7.

3. The New York Yankees currently hold the most World Series titles with.

4. Hot dogs are the most popular food item sold at Major League Baseball ballparks. Over 21 million hot dogs were sold at MLB stadiums in 2014.

5. The longest Major League Baseball game on record occurred on May 9, 1984, between the Chicago White Sox and Milwaukee Brewers. The game lasted 8 hours, 6 minutes. The most innings played in a Major League Baseball game was 26 on May 1, 1920, between the Brooklyn Dodgers and Boston Braves.

6. .

7. The mound to home plate distance is 60 feet, 6 inches.

8. Before they can be used in a Major League Baseball game, each MLB baseball is rubbed with special mud to improve

grip and reduce luster. This special mud comes from a specific, secret location in the state of New Jersey.

9. The fastest Major League Baseball game on record took place on September 28, 1919. The game between the New York Giants and Philadelphia Phillies took 51 minutes. An average MLB game is about 3 hours.

10. The American League uses a designated hitter. A DH only hits and does not play in the field. In the National League, the pitcher hits instead of using a designated hitter. If an interleague game is being played, whether a DH is used or not is determined by which team is the home team. If the home team is from the American League, each team will use a DH. If the home team is from the National League, each team's pitcher will hit.

11. The distance between bases is 90 feet.

CONCLUSION

Learn anything new? Now you truly are the ultimate Twins fan! Not only did you learn about the Twins of the modern era, but you also expanded your knowledge back to the early days of the franchise.

You learned about the Twins' origins as the Washington Senators and their history. You learned about the history of their uniforms and jersey numbers and read some of the craziest nicknames of all time. You learned more about the legendary Rod Carew and Bert Blyleven. You also learned about the Hall of Famers Harmon Killebrew and Kirby Puckett. You were amazed by Twins' stats and recalled some of the most famous Twins trades, drafts, and draft picks of all time.

You broke down your knowledge by outfielders, infielders, pitchers, and catchers. You looked back on the Twins' championships and playoff feats and the awards that came before, after, and during them. You also learned about the Twins' fiercest rivalries, both within their division and outside it.

Every team in the MLB has a storied history, but the Minnesota Twins have one of the most memorable of all. They have won three World Series championships with the backing of their devoted fans. Being the ultimate Twins fan takes knowledge and a whole lot of patience, which you tested with this book. Whether you knew every answer or were stumped by several questions, you learned some of the most interesting history that the game of baseball has to offer.

The deep history of the Minnesota Twins franchise represents what we all love about the game of baseball. The heart, the determination, the tough times, and the unexpected moments, plus the players who inspire us and encourage us to do our best, because even if you get knocked down, there is always another game and another day.

With players like Jose Berríos, Max Kepler, and Miguel Sano, the future for the Twins continues to look bright. They have a lot to prove but there is no doubt that this franchise will continue to be one of the most competitive teams in Major League Baseball year after year.

It's a new decade, which means there is a clean slate, ready to continue writing the history of the Minnesota Twins. The ultimate Twins fan cannot wait to see what's to come for their beloved boys from the Twin Cities.

Made in the USA
Coppell, TX
12 June 2023

18013987R00090